The Mouse Family

Fun with Words

by Rosalind Sutton

Illustrated by Pamela Storey

Brimax Books · Newmarket · England

Washing

On Monday the mice are washing,
It is a busy day;
Some socks, some shirts and dungarees,
There is no time for play.

Reading

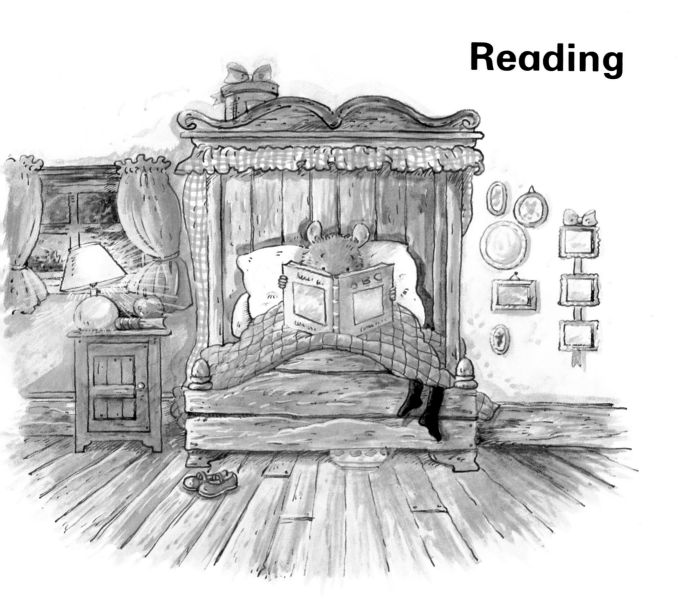

At bedtime Flo is reading,
Before she goes to sleep;
She tucks herself up tight in bed,
And learns her ABC.

Digging

Out digging on a Tuesday,
The mice are clearing weeds;
There is a lot of work to do
Before they plant their seeds.

Walking

Out walking in the afternoon,
The mice are holding hands;
They love to chatter as they walk
Along the golden sands.

Baking

On Wednesday the mice are baking,
Crisp cookies fill the tray;
Don and Archie help themselves,
So they are sent away.

Fishing

Fishing in the afternoon,
Is what the mice like best;
They settle by the river bank,
With fishing lines and nets.

Shopping

On Thursday the mice go shopping,
To buy some tasty cheese,
They also buy some fruit and nuts,
Some carrots and some peas.

Carrying

Now all the mice are carrying,
A very heavy load;
Each has a bag of shopping
As they walk along the road.

Eating

The mice are eating supper,
And all of them agree;
That there is nothing better,
Than golden, toasted cheese.

Cleaning

On Friday the mice are cleaning,
Each mouse has work to do;
Sweeping, dusting and polishing,
There's so much to get through.

Sliding

Sliding on a helter skelter,
Going round and round;
The mice slide from the very top,
Until they reach the ground.

Playing

That night the mice are playing,
Together they all stand;
With fiddle, drums and xylophone,
They have their own small band.

Swimming

On Saturday the mice decide,
That they would like some fun;
They all go swimming in the lake,
Then dry out in the sun.

Climbing

Now all the mice are climbing trees,
They climb up very high;
They use their tails to hold on tight,
And seem to touch the sky.

Swinging

Don is swinging on a rope,
He's swinging high and low;
The others come and watch him play,
They want to have a go.

Jogging

Going jogging on a Sunday,
Is what the mice like best;
But Don and Archie run too fast,
And have to stop to rest.

Sailing

The mice are sailing on the sea,
In a boat all of their own;
They float along all afternoon,
Then Archie rows them home.

Sleeping

The mice are sleeping in their beds,
It's very late at night;
And outside in the sky above,
The moon is shining bright.